Surviving Life with Laughter

by

Steve Kissell

For Pete,
the Big Wheel in my life.

Contents

APPENDIX

1

It Hurts So Good!

The Physiological Effects of Laughter

Some patients, though conscious that their condition is perilous, recover their health simply through their contentment with the goodness of the physician.   Hippocrates, 460-400 BCE

H ave you ever wondered why you feel so good during and after a prolonged laugh? Why is it that our problems seem unimportant when we are concentrating on drawing our next breath? The answer is very simple - laughter has many wonderful and beneficial effects on the human body. Consider the following data: While the body is busy convulsing uncontrollably with laughter, our respiratory system is stimulated. Lungs are stretched and cleaned. It is a matter of scientific fact that air has been recorded leaving the body at more than 70 miles per hour! As the air rushes out, so do contaminants that somehow worked their way into the body.

In addition to the "housecleaning effect," oxygenated air enters the body at an increased rate. The result: in comes the good air and out goes the bad! If more air comes into the system, more oxygen will invariably boost the body's energy level.

The positive effects of laughter also work on the cardiovascular system. Laughing increases the heart rate and helps raise the blood pressure as well. How can an elevated blood pressure be helpful? After laughter subsides, blood pressure dips down either below or back to its former level. A good healthy laugh keeps the circulation flowing and enables the heart to work harder. This is especially good for patients who have just undergone surgery. Mind the stitches!

Muscle and skeletal tension are greatly reduced during a good belly laugh. Have you noticed how impossible it is to continue climbing those apartment steps while carrying a mattress when you and your fellow movers are overcome with laughter? Laughter has a wonderful way of taking over the body! And laughter definitely has an impact on reducing tension. During a "spastic laugh," the chest, legs, arms, and even the facial muscles get a much needed workout.

Hearty laughter is rumored to be responsible for releasing endorphines, which are the body's natural painkillers. These chemicals are known to be much more powerful than morphine. So, on those days that you find yourself waking up with a backache and telling yourself, "I can't make the donuts," there is relief in sight! An early morning laugh will reduce the pain simply by taking your mind off the problem.

The well-known humor lecturer Norman Cousins coined the phrase "internal jogging." He was referring to the exercise that our organs receive during a hearty laugh. Another side effect of the internal jogging is the massage sent to our intestines. The entire digestive tract is stimulated through the exercise brought on by laughter. For post-operative patients or others who are confined to bed, this is a wonderful form of assistance that helps the natural digestive processes. Have you ever wondered why we have after-dinner speeches and not before-dinner speeches? The inventor of the term was aware of the beneficial effects of laughter on the digestive system. You could eliminate (excuse the pun) laxatives and bran all together just by incorporating laughter with each meal!!

So, there you have it! The wonderful effects of laughter on the body. But, of course, you already knew that it made you feel better! Laughter is inexpensive; it won't make you fat; it makes you feel "high"; it's great exercise, and it's legal! Quick! Use laughter as much as possible before the government finds a way to tax it!

During the 1970s Norman Cousins was diagnosed with a painful connective-tissue disorder and given the odds of 500 to

1 to recover. However, Cousins had an interesting theory. His theory was that if he allowed himself to become unhappy, he would become worse! In reverse, if he became happier, then he should get better! With his doctor's permission, he checked out of the hospital and into a nearby hotel. He asked his friends to bring him television shows like *Candid Camera*, *Lucille Ball* and Groucho Marx films. Cousins and his friends shared jokes, riddles, and puns - anything to make him laugh. He discovered that for every ten minutes of laughter he was able to sleep for two pain-free hours. This led him to make future studies on humor and disease, and eventually he fully recovered from his disorder.

While he was in the hospital for testing, a nurse brought Cousins a plastic cup and asked for a urine specimen. After the nurse left, he poured apple juice into the cup. When she returned, the nurse commented that the specimen was cloudy. He replied, "It sure is. Let's run it through again!" . . . And he proceeded to drink it down! Rumor has it that she left nursing and went into another field of work!

Norman Cousins laid the foundation for today's humorists. With his early exploration of humor and medicine Cousins can certainly be considered the Lewis and Clark of the humor-health industry.

Voltaire said: "It's the physician's job to entertain the patient while he heals." Today you can find many humorous activities in hospitals throughout the country. Many medical institutions are organizing "Humor Rooms" filled with such

things as comedy tapes, games, and toys. Ruth Hamilton, of the Carolina Health and Humor Association, has invented a humor cart that travels around the hospital wards carrying juggling equipment, funny books, and tapes. This cart, aptly named the "Laughmobile," has proven to be very beneficial for patients and staff at several prestigious hospitals.

A surgical nurse told me about an incident in which a patient was due for surgery. Discovering that the surgeon was an avid golfer, the nurse quickly wrote on a Post-it note: "Please replace all divots!" and stuck it to the area to be operated on. She also told a story of a post-surgery nurse who was changing a bandage on a patient whose toe had recently been removed because of diabetes. As she unwrapped the foot, she saw the missing toe and commented to the patient, "My goodness, Joan, I see one of the piggies didn't make it back from the market!"

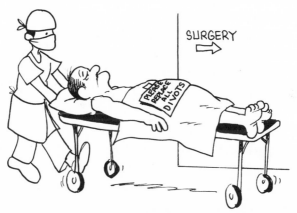

I have a friend I'll call Josh (because that's his name) who was hospitalized after an automobile accident. Fortunately, Josh suffered no internal injuries, but he had major muscle spasms because of the collision. Because Josh was accustomed to being very active, he soon became depressed. However, his depression soon lifted when an attractive nurse stopped by to give him a bath. She arrived with a warm bowl of soapy water, a sponge, and a smile. She washed Josh's arms, face, chest and stomach. Then she washed his feet and legs and, to his surprise, gave him the sponge and said, "Now, it's your turn!" So he took the sponge and washed her face and arms and...! What fun Josh had that day sharing the story with his friends. It really lifted his spirits.

A local clown club in Norfolk, Virginia, regularly visits a children's ward in a hospital. Once each week patients look forward to personal visits from colorful characters with names such as "Sunshine," "Merry Heart," "Dr. E.K.G." The clowns are volunteers who give their time to bring laughter and joy to sick children who are bored or scared. The clowns bring puppets, toys, and magic tricks to delight and lift the spirits of little hearts.

I recently read about an activities director of a nursing home who started a "Joke Line." Each week a resident wrote or borrowed a joke and recorded it on an answering machine. Then residents merely had to dial J-O-K-E for some good humor, and the telephone "celebrities" had a ball recording the jokes!

As with all good things, there always seems to be at least one negative factor. And the negative factor involved with laughter could be a very important one to you! I had just completed a seminar on humor in the workplace when a woman approached me from the audience and told me that she laughed until she leaked! So, you see, laughter can cause us to lose control of certain body functions. Of course, if you have been around kids, you know all about that.

2
Two Wrongs Don't Make A Right, But Two Rights Make An Airplane!

The Psychological Effects of Laughter

The human race has only one really effective weapon and that is laughter. Humor is the great thing, the saving thing, after all. The minute it crops up, all our hardnesses yield, all our irritations and resentments slip away, and a sunny spirit takes their place. (Mark Twain)

I believe that one of the most beneficial effects of laughter is in communication. It can distract us from our problems, and it can also break the cycle of anger.

One beautiful sunny morning I was traveling to work in bumper-to-bumper traffic. I soon found myself banging on my watch hoping that it would break or slow down so that I wouldn't be late for work. All of a sudden a car pulled up and, without signaling, pulled in front of me. Of course, the driver found that there wasn't enough room in there for his car and jammed on his brakes. I, too, had to do the same thing to avoid a rear-end collision. I was fuming!! My neck and face turned red, and my knuckles turned white as I gripped the steering wheel in a death grip. I wanted to pull out in traffic and show him that I was number one in the driving championships! (After all, now I would be 20 feet late for work!) Then it came to me. Why should I let that guy control my workday? If I arrived at work in a foul mood, the day would not be as productive for me. However, I knew that I would feel much better if I received immediate and satisfying revenge. What did I do? While reaching in the glovebox, I signaled and pulled out in traffic beside him. I located my emergency Groucho Marx glasses and put them on, and gave him a friendly wave as I passed by! He laughed so hard he nearly drove off the road!

Analyzing the situation later, I realized what had happened. The discourteous driver had cut me off and controlled my life in a negative way by making me angry. I, on the other hand, had affected his life in a positive way by making him laugh. He would probably get to work and tell all his co-workers about the wacko he saw on the interstate. I could also share with my colleagues a funny story about my trip to work.

I remember with fond memories a short trip with a couple named Jim and Barbara. I brought three pairs of Groucho glasses to flash travelers on the highway. Folks were cracking up and having a great time. I noticed that Barbara wasn't wearing hers, and when I asked her why she, replied, "Because I am afraid someone will recognize me!" I reassured her that she wouldn't be recognized. Everyone on the highway was having a great time with our antics until some teenagers pulled up beside us. They were, of course, truly dismayed that adults would actually try to make them laugh and were, in fact, having fun at their expense. Our car pulled ahead of theirs, and after a few minutes I noticed a flash of white out of the corner of my eye. I turned to see the car with the teenagers once again beside us. This time they had hastily drawn a sign in the window that said "geeks" and were pointing at us and laughing. Barbara then said, "What's a geek?" (She works at a private school.) I told her we were. To me it didn't matter whether the kids were laughing at us or with us; at least they were laughing.

Stephanie, a family friend, graduated from the University of North Carolina. She told me that the most embarrassing time of her life was walking to school through fraternity row. I

asked her if the guys did the typical boyish catcalls and whistles. She said that, unfortunately, what they did was make scorecards and hold them up as the girls passed by. What really made Stephanie mad was that she never managed to score well. I inquired how she dealt with this embarrassing situation. She told me that she got together with the sorority sisters; they made their own signs to use on the boys, but they used negative numbers! After this, the guys lost all interest in bothering the girls any further. Laughter is indeed a wonderful communicator!

If you ask police officers in your city what is their most dangerous call, I'm sure they will tell you it is a domestic dispute. Two officers were making such a call, and as they were approaching the house, a portable television set came crashing out the dining room window and exploded on the front lawn. The officers didn't miss a beat and knocked on the door. When the angry husband asked who it was, they answered, "TV repairman!" The man inside was shocked! He anticipated a physical confrontation, but instead a human bond was formed.

I once stayed in a hotel in Williamsburg, Virginia, which left a small note to their guests about towel snatching. It read: "*Some time ago we received word that several of our towels were being kidnapped and taken to far-away places. Now that we have new ones, we are a family again. You wouldn't want to break up a happy family, would you? Thanks for caring.*" I should also mention that the note had a cartoon drawing of a happy towel family. The note really appealed to me and I felt sorry for the broken family. So I took them all home with me!

I once saw a sign in a telephone booth with a picture of Superman on it. From time to time vandals would tear up the booth and a homeless man who used the booth to sleep in lost his bed until the booth was repaired. Because he was such a creative person, he made a sign that said, "Dear Friend, please don't vandalize my booth as I have no other place to change. Thanks. Your friend, Superman." From what I understand, all damages to the booth stopped. Isn't it wonderful what a little humor can do.

Patty Wooten, R.N., is a humor consultant from San Francisco, and she says that "laughter is a servant to us. It reduces anxiety and tension. It provides a socially acceptable release for angry, hostile, and aggressive emotions and feelings of frustration. Humor "breaks the ice" and reduces the fear of unfamiliar settings. It also helps establish warm interpersonal relationships and trust. It allows us a detached and expanded perspective on our problems which can enhance creativity. It also lifts morale, inspires hope, builds team spirit and cohesion. It energizes us physically and relaxes us emotionally in many of the same ways that exercise does."

Laughter does indeed assist in reducing tension. I recently read about an office secretary who was being harassed by her supervisor. He was a "sweater gazer" in the workplace, and she wanted him to treat her in a professional manner and not leer at her. She also knew that he controlled her evaluations which, ultimately, affected her salary. However, this was no ordinary secretary, and one day she brought in some supplies purchased from an arts-and-crafts store. At the store she found those real-looking eyes, you know, the kind that wiggle back and forth? After sewing them on her sweater in strategic places, she put her coat on and left for work. That morning, while taking a letter, she noticed that her boss was once again leering at her sweater. Without giving it a second thought, she stood up, turned away and removed her coat. She then turned back around and said, "I am so glad that we have finally made eye contact!!!" Did she get fired? Hardly. Did he get the point? Yes! Once again humor triumphs as a wonderful form of communication.

Following are a few fun definitions for you to put in your humor diary. You are keeping one, aren't you?

HUMOR: openness to being fully human.

HUMORIZE: bring joy and laughter to a too-serious situation.

SILLY: from Greek; *selig*: blessed, healthy, happy, and prosperous.

COMIC STYLE: your own personal way of expressing humor.

HUMOR INHIBITOR: anything that stops the natural flow of laughter and joy.

HUMOR RITUAL: a daily repetitive act that instills the sillies.

HUMOR SYSTEM: a program for keeping humor going in the workplace and in personal life.

BUTTSHAKE: a fun way to greet a friend!

Laughter is said to assist in connecting the right and left sides of the brain. Stress can break that connection, and laughter can assist in the re-connecting. A whole brain is certainly more advantageous than half a brain, wouldn't you think? Combining the logical side and the creative side aid in solving problems and challenges that face each of us every day.

Doyne Miche, a retired Presbyterian minister in Atlanta, says that laughter is a "now emotion." That is, if we are laughing, we can't worry about such problems as our daughter going on her first date or our son driving the car for the first time. You can even forget to worry about your mother-in-law showing up at the door with two suitcases in her hands. Laughter can help us forget all our problems. Doyne also shared with me a great tip to reduce stress after a busy day at work. He says he stands in front of his full length mirror naked. If that doesn't make him chuckle, he jumps up and down to see what wiggles! What a hoot he is!

Dr. Annette Goodheart, noted humorist and speaker, tells us that laughter can "assist us with dealing with fear; you can't be afraid when you are laughing. Angels fly because they take themselves lightly!" She also says that "laughter is non-reasonable, logical, and rational. We can't do anything else while we laugh...we can't worry about our problems." She

19

ventures to give us some important insights:

Laughter lets us re-focus on what is important to us.

Laughter is the release of the experience.

Everyone is out to play; they are just waiting to come out.

If you laugh a lot, no one will take you seriously.

The more a people are oppressed, the more they laugh; it is a tool of defense.

It's always your choice to laugh or cry.

The constitution tells us to be happy!

Audio tapes are a wonderful source of laughter while you drive to work or do some serious traveling. I often travel by car, and when I am driving, I listen to a variety of interesting subjects. It is a great way to learn and reaffirm what I already know or what I have forgotten. Zig Ziglar tells us that motivation is like taking a shower. You just can't get by with one; you need it every day!

You may remember the "masking" techniques that were popular some years ago? That's when the producer of the tape or record inserts a message backward and your subconscious somehow picks it up. Now they have subliminal tapes that tell you how great you are while you listen to the sound of the ocean or music. This technique allows you to sleep while the tape tells you wonderful things about yourself. I became suspicious of this, and I slowed the tape down and found that it was saying..."Buy more tapes, buy more tapes, buy more tapes!"

3
Humor Thy
Mother and Father
(The Fourth Commandment)

Spirituality of Humor

A merry heart doeth good like a medicine, but a broken spirit drieth the bones.

Proverbs 11:22

When we speak of the spirituality of humor, we are not implying that we should be entertained in church, although church and synagogue are great places in which to laugh. The spirituality of humor implies the spiritualness inside each of our hearts, the ability to have compassion, love, and passion for work and play.

The type of person that you are deep down inside is very important. Where are you spiritually when it comes to the subject of laughter? Not necessarily in the godly sense, but who are you really in your heart? What sort of person do others perceive or judge you to be?

Let's say that you are at a parade, and the farm animals are passing by. It goes without saying that horses leave items in the road - items for which they no longer have any use. There you have it-horse manure on the parade route. Suddenly, a clown emerges from nowhere and gleefully places a plastic red rose in the center of this pile. Are you aghast? Is that obscene? Surely something which originates from the backside of an animal should not be toyed with; it should be ignored! Or, perhaps, you're thinking, "Hey, fertilizer--flower!" Something negative turns into something positive. Suddenly a marching band of children appears and spots the manure marked by the rose, which is now easily avoided. It is all in how you perceive the situation.

Looking at the negative or looking at the positive in all situations can be a benefit to your health and to the attitudes of those around you. A family friend named June had diabetes and eventually lost one of her legs. After recovering from surgery and receiving an artificial limb, she and her husband came for a visit. June asked if she could see the new bedrooms that we had just built on the second floor. Her husband John suggested that we carry her upstairs in a two-man fireman carry. So, as we crossed our arms and linked our hands together, June hopped into them. We began to climb the stairs. After reaching the top, we started to set her down and realized that her artificial leg was still downstairs! Apparently, when we picked her up, the artificial limb stayed right there in the middle of the living room floor. After realizing the mistake, both John and I turned beet red with embarrassment. June looked at us both and said, "I haven't got a leg to stand on!"

What wonderful courage and spirit this friend had. She saw how uncomfortable we were and made fun of herself to make us feel more at ease. What wonderful passion June had for life! Later, after she passed away, her husband had the service videotaped for her parents who were too ill and elderly to travel. At the conclusion of the service, friends of June's were invited into the pastor's study to record on camera a message for her parents. I, of course, shared the story of the leg. I felt that her parents needed to know what courage June had and what a blessing it was just to know her.

I believe that laughter can help us all endure the grieving process. If we laugh all through life, why must we be so serious in death?

I remember four things in particular about my father's death and funeral. I was just sixteen, in geography class in a small rural school in Arcadia, Ohio, when a messenger brought a note to me from the office. It simply said, "You're needed at home right away." I knew that my mother would not send for me unless it were an emergency. And although my father was recovering from open-heart surgery that day, I wondered if someone else in the family was injured. Perhaps if my thoughts were not on Dad, he would somehow be all right.

Pulling into the driveway, I saw Mom standing in the doorway with tears in her eyes. She said, "I'm sorry, Steve, it's your Dad. He died early this morning." The image of her standing there and the words she said will stay with me forever. Death is so difficult to understand at sixteen. . . or any age.

The second event that remains with me is sitting in the front row near Dad's casket at the funeral service. I could do nothing but stare at the floor. I can still see the tears splashing down on the tops of my shoes. It seemed that they traveled in slow motion, spattering the leather and carrying the dust to the carpet.

The service was a blur, there were so many friends and relatives. I was impressed that my father had so many friends. He was indeed a man who was loved by many. When it came time to carry the casket to the hearse, I was very proud to serve as a pallbearer. I remember lifting up on the handle high so that I could carry more weight than the others. I wanted more of the burden than anyone else. He was my father; I was his son.

The graveside images do not reappear to me. The fourth significant thing I recall was the dinner. The family and friends had gathered for a feast to celebrate Dad's life and death. I sat beside my uncle, who was my father's closest living relative except his mother. Conversations centered around sports, the weather, where everyone now lived, and what jobs they had. They were talking about everything but Dad, to try to deal with their grief. Perhaps by discussing other topics it would not seem that they had gathered to bury my father.

Something came over me. Glancing at my uncle, I saw that he was looking at me at the same moment. For some odd reasons, I put my hands to my neck, pulled out the skin on each side, and said, "Excuse me. Can I get another spoon for my coffee?" My uncle's face immediately contorted in laughter, and pandemonium broke out at the table.

Several more comical facial expressions followed with a re-telling of every joke and amusing story about my father that came to mind. Those at the table were in tears of laughter, and others at different tables began to laugh simply because we did. Even Grandma could not keep from laughing at this seemingly solemn affair. What started as a small joke, a grasp at something to do or say, evolved into a release.

We all felt better after laughing. That was our way of dealing with our grief with our grief; a cleansing and cathartic process had indeed transpired. Little did I know that what I discovered that day would follow me and influence others many years down the road.

Where am I now, and how do I deal with the grief? It has been 21 years since my father's death and I still cry. When I am in my hometown of Tiffin, Ohio, I visit relatives and friends of my father, and we cry together. My children and wife have visited his grave, yet they can never fully realize what a truly remarkable man they missed knowing.

I have wonderful times reminiscing about my Dad's life, and often find myself quoting his expressions like, "Take that apart!" That is what he would say when he saw something unbelievable. When he was tired, he would often flop on the couch and say, "I'm not going to fight it!" and take a quick catnap. But most of all, I remember his famous and widely used, "You gotta press on!"

Well, Dad, I am pressing on, remembering always the laughs and practical jokes that you shared with friends and strangers. I believe laughter can help in the grieving process, if it is given the chance. We laugh through life, and we can laugh through death.

A few years ago, a dear friend lost his father. I was able to relate to him and shared the story of my father's funeral. Here is his reply:

Dear Steve,

It was nice seeing you again and having a few moments to exchange a few jokes. I was not as close to my father as you must have been, but I appreciate the thoughts that you penned so eloquently in your letter. My father's funeral was a little unusual, however. His long-time pastor started the eulogy by telling several jokes. One of them was about a Baptist man that had died. The family needed to have their pastor bury him properly but their own Baptist preacher was out of town. A local Methodist minister was asked to fill in. He agreed to do the service if it was permitted by his denominational leaders. So he phoned his superior to ask if it was okay to bury the Baptist. After several moments of silence, his superior answered with, "Yes, bury all the Baptists you can." I thought, "Has the pastor lost his mind?" "Did he pick up the wrong speech by mistake?" This was a funeral not a celebrity roast! As the service continued the point he had wanted to make became clear. My father was known for cheering people up with his jokes and funny stories. What better way to remember him than in the very way that he had lived, with joy and laughter. My father was a Christian and the lid of his casket had the words •Going Home• printed on it. Even though there is always grief when a loved one passes on, it is comforting to know that they are "going home" to a better place. Sometimes we laugh to keep from crying. You are right, Steve, the proper kind of humor can act as a release for the grief. Thanks for sharing your letter with me.

In His Service,

R.G. Dewey

P.S. Excuse me. Can I get another spoon for my coffee?

God truly has a great sense of humor. Take the dandelion, for example. What a practical joke that was on mankind. Every sunny weekend one can spot thousands of deranged people flailing away at them with shovels, picks, and sprays.

You see, in the beginning, God created the Earth, and he was well pleased. The oceans were vast, the mountains tall, and the trees sturdy. He created many great animals, and He created man and woman. God looked at what he had done, and was well pleased. However, He still felt there was something missing. Something soft, colorful, and perhaps gentle.

So God called upon the angel of the flowers and asked her to put the finishing touches on what he had done. The angel agreed that the Earth needs something small and gentle, perhaps for the children. So the angel went to work and decided she would plant roses. "Oh, please plant us near a castle," said the roses. "You see, we are very delicate and need protection and we would like to be picked by a princess some day." The forget-me-nots said, "Please plant us in the woods where we will be protected from the hot sun. We need to grow in the shade." It was the lilies' turn and they said, "Oh, we will only bloom for one day, and if we are picked, we will fade very fast. Plant us where we will be seen but not picked."

The angel of the flowers then turned to the dandelions and asked, "Where do you want to be planted?" The dandelions said, "Oh, we will bloom and be happy wherever we are planted. Plant us in the fields where the children play. Let the children dance on our pretty golden faces. Let them pick us and carry us home. And when we fade, they can play with our fluffy heads. We want to be the children's flower." God has even managed to put them in between the cracks of sidewalks, the homeowner's favorite place.

The following announcements were taken from church and synagogue bulletins. You can be the judge as to whether they are misprints, typographical errors, or whatever:

There will be a meeting of the little mothers club on Tuesday. All wishing to become little mothers, please meet the pastor in his study.

The women of the church have cast off clothing of every kind and they may be seen in the church basement on Saturday afternoon.

Baptism today will be held in both wings and children may be baptized at both ends.

The literary society will meet on Thursday. Mrs. Branigan will sing "Put me in my bed" accompanied by the pastor.

There will be no healings this Wednesday due to the pastor's illness.

Mrs. Johansen has had her phone changed to an unlisted number due to harassing calls. Her new number is 547-8401.

You may now find yourself looking more closely at your bulletins at your place of worship. Who promised you that after reading this chapter your next outing would be a safe one and you would arrive at your destination alive? This could be your last laugh!

P.S. Remember, God loves to hear His children laugh.

4
Is There Laughter After Marriage?

Laughing together can be a time of intimacy and communion, a time when we come forward, fully present, and touch into each other's humanness and vulnerability. Humor is a way that we express our humility. By joining in humor and acknowledging our oneness, we can have a profound experience of unity and cooperation. When we laugh with another, we enfold that person in our loving, reach out with caring, understanding, and support. That in itself may be one of the most profound expressions of healing energy of which we are capable.

Barry Sultanoff, M.D.

I f anyone ever predicted that I would marry an Italian girl from New York and live in a state where people eat hush puppies and say things like "Tuesday week" and "I just carried my mother to the store," my reply would have been, "Where is the hidden camera? Am I on TV? Is this a joke?"

A dear friend would be proud of me, though. She is the one who introduced me to my future wife. I was new in town and in the Navy and met Martha while she was working at a supply center for the government. I told her that I had just arrived in the area and was single. She quickly told me that she was waiting for a new roommate to arrive and would ask her if she wanted to go out on a date with me. The roommate's reply was a surprising "No." Undaunted, I went to meet her to ask her out in person. Unbelievably, she said "No" again! I came back a week later, and I think that because I was such a pest, she agreed to go out with me.

From that day on, my world began to spin in another direction, and I fell madly in love with Alice. After a few short months, I managed to find the courage to ask her to marry me. Guess what she said? "No." Are you surprised? Now it was time to up the ante. I informed her right then and there that I was the last eligible male Kissell left and that she should not pass up an opportunity like this. Sometime later she came to her senses and asked me to marry her! Now we share a wonderful life together with our three children, one of each. I have been married for 15 years now. Just think: a guy only gets five to ten for murder these days!!

The most important suggestion for anyone contemplating marriage is to marry your best friend. I can honestly say that I did, and it makes all the difference in the world! We have had only one big fight and that was on our wedding day. She wanted to be in the pictures!

Statistics tell us that half of the marriages today will end in divorce. How can we explain these dismal numbers, especially since all divorces have something in common--they all began with marriage! You could say that marriage is like the Navy--everyone complains, but there seems to be an incredible number of reenlistments! How do we explain this phenomenon? Well, since I'm not a marriage counselor or a sociologist, I can speak only from my own marital adventure--and, boy, what an adventure it is. That's why, from where I stand, the most important bond is that special bond of friendship that exists in **ALL** good marriages. Because, quite frankly folks, if you're not friends or if you don't **LIKE** the person you're married to, it will never work. Fortunately, Alice and I are each other's best friend--and what a wonderful feeling that is in a relationship. Speaking for myself, friendship and the fact that you really like this person, will take you through the worst of times and the best of times!

Besides friendship and really liking the person you are going to marry, another area of concern is, "Would you mind being financially ruined by this person?" At this point, readers, I would imagine that I have your complete attention, and I will continue with my suggestions for a "model" marriage!!

Have you heard someone say that they are getting really "serious" in a relationship? Why do we have to be serious about our love life? We need to learn to laugh and enjoy our mates more freely. Your love should free up your feelings, which should allow you to have more fun with your relationship. Loosen up and laugh!

A woman once told me that she and her husband went to a secluded hotel for their twentieth anniversary. When they had settled into their room, she went into the bathroom, undressed completely, and donned a pair of Groucho Marx glasses. Her attempt at humor really surprised her husband. Much to her surprise he insisted that she wear them to bed! Hey, whatever works and makes magic in your marriage shouldn't be challenged.

I can recall some very funny moments with my wife, Alice. Arriving home early one summer day, I found my companion in the kitchen, making those wonderful succulent watermelon balls without the seeds. I must have startled her because the watermelon shot off the counter and hit the floor. If you know anything about the laws of physics, you know that watermelons explode on impact, especially on kitchen floors. There was juice, seeds, and red stuff flying all over the kitchen, and I began to laugh uncontrollably! I was laughing so hard that I couldn't breathe. I soon found myself on the kitchen floor writhing in painful laughter. She, however, failed to see the humor in this situation and actually became angry. Then she said to me in her most serious voice, "How would you like to not see me for three days?" This question merely added more reason to laugh uncontrollably, which I continued

to do for a while longer. I really began to understand the seriousness of the situation when I finally was able to stop laughing. Most importantly, the swelling in both my eyes did go down after three days, and I could once again see my lovely bride!

Another special moment of humor in our lives came early one morning, very early. The alarm clock went off at 5:00 a.m. I was not happy. Even though I am a motivational humorist, which in case you're wondering is a "clown with a tie on," I was not pleased about the early time when the alarm went off. My wife nudged me several times and seemed to delight in the fact that she had another two hours of sleep. I can hear her sweet voice now as she said, "C'mon, Mr. Motivation, it's time to get up!" I particularly remember climbing out of bed and discovering why God made toes--to find the furniture, which somehow magically moves during the night! After several choice comments, I heard my beautiful and adoring wife say, "Well, Mr. Humor, can't find anything to laugh about this morning?" A courtroom scene from a Perry Mason show flashed in my mind: would it be justifiable homicide?

I can honestly say, though, that my wife and I both have a knack of making each other laugh at a moment's notice. A simple reminder of an infamous dinner party brings uncontrollable and delightful laughter to both of us. We were invited to a friend's house for dinner, and I found myself in the kitchen snooping around the stove, trying to find out what was to be served. As I lifted one of the lids, I discovered too late a lot of spilled cooking grease on the floor in front of the stove. My shoe soles were quickly covered with the slippery substance. Without further hesitation, I began to skate about the kitchen floor until my wife stepped into the kitchen to see what I was up to. She knows me well! Now, it was her turn to burst into uncontrollable laughter. Now, whenever she pops into the kitchen to check me while I cook, I begin to skate about, bringing hilarious memories to both of us.

I can still remember the pastor who married us whispering for me to turn around and face the people. There I was with my best man, Pete, at the altar of a small Methodist church in Babylon, New York. I was staring at the pastor, and he kept whispering to me to turn around and face the congregation as my bride-to-be approached the altar on her father's arm. It was then that I realized that she was very serious about going through with this wedding!! I think there was only one other time in my life when I had a similar feeling, and that was when I went bungee jumping! Looking down from 150 feet with a rubberband on your ankles is just like looking down the aisle at your future mate. All time stands still, and life as you know it ceases to exist.

It seemed an eternity before she finally stood beside me, and the next thing I knew I was dancing with her at the reception! We have had a wonderful relationship. We may differ in many ways, but that seems to give our marriage flavor. As an example, Alice is an excellent vacationer. She has mastered the art of total relaxation. I, on the other hand, have never been able to grasp the concept of time out. My wife is perfectly content basking in the sun on a lounge chair reading a romance novel. Can you believe that she highlights certain passages for me to read later? She is also an excellent money manager. I, on the other hand, am surprised when I do not receive a monthly letter from the bank stating that I have been bad again.

We're also alike in many ways. We are both very romantic, leaving love notes for the other to find. Taking candlelight bubble baths (sometimes even together) is a favorite, or sharing a chocolate sundae with two spoons and even splitting the cherry in half.

She graduated from college suma cum laud, I graduated Thank You Laud! She completed college in four years. I on the other hand, graduated in six. But, hey, I really wanted that Associate Degree!

We both have an incredible love and admiration for our

children, although we have thought at times they were both switched at birth. How could we have possibly given life to these unique wonders.

I wish you well, my friend, as you set out to find your best friend in life to share your laughter and joy with. And if you are fortunate to have already found your spouse, I hope God continues to bless you with friendship, love, and a very important sense of humor!

And please try to remember, never kiss your spouse on an empty stomach. Behind the ears or on the hands or lips, but never on an empty stomach.

P.S. And don't ever forget this: Never laugh and point at the same time!

5
Practicing "Safe Stress"

The phone rings incessantly; your boss wants three jobs done right now; you've been interrupted numerous times; and it isn't even noon! During lunch, you run a half dozen errands, gobble your food down, and rush back to work. Five o'clock comes; it's rush hour traffic, a quick stop at the grocery store and then to the day-care center to pick up the kids. Dinner is a frenzied microwave affair; "quality time" with the kids is a disaster, and by 9:00 p.m. you're tired, depressed, and not feeling good!!

Sound familiar? It's called stress, and if you think you're the only one who has it, think again! Experts say that stress costs the American economy millions annually in lower productivity, absenteeism, and stress-related disabilities. Also, stress accounts for approximately 75 percent of all visits to doctors and emergency centers! Seventy-five percent!! As a nation we need to practice "safe stress"!

Stress has become a national malady which can be attributed to many factors. If there seems to be more stress in our society, you're right. Time magazine recently reported on research by pollster Louis Harris which showed that leisure time enjoyed by Americans has shrunk by 37 percent since 1973, while the average work week has grown from 41 to 47 hours. Another survey revealed that 73 percent of the women interviewed and 51 percent of the men complained of too many responsibilities and too little time off from work.

Other symptoms of stress are revealed daily and sometimes hourly in both the print and visual media. Movies, television, newspapers, and magazines bombard us with graphic details about the fears and frustrations that plague our society today. Think about it: in years past when we went to a movie, it would often inspire or lift up our spirits. Today when we leave a theater, how do we feel? More stressed out and put-upon? Where we once received solace and a respite from the day's events, we are reminded often about the troubles in our world.

There is probably no way we can escape the realities of living in the 1990s and all the stress that comes along with this. But what we can do, in a very positive manner, is to take back some of the control that we have relinquished as we have tried to assimilate new roles in our quickly changing society. Stress is a very serious problem in our country. But with some simple methods of relaxation and by injecting humor into difficult situations, we can once again feel in control. And when we are in control, don't we feel better?

We can't hide from the world, so we need to acquire the proper "tools" that will enable us to live as stress-free as possible--and it is possible!!

According to Dr. Robert Richards, "Stress could be defined as the rate of wear and tear on our bodies. Stress is any intimidating force that frightens, provokes, or threatens the body. Any event that alters our body's systems could be classified as stress or a stressor."

Stress is related to high blood pressure and heart problems, and it may cause cancer. One popular theory states that we all have a cancer or cancers in our bodies and that stress can actually activate the onslaught of the disease. Think about people you know who have either died of cancer or who now have it: have they been exposed to some sort of tragedy in their lives during the past 12 months? Sadness brought on from a loss, whether it be the loss of a mate through divorce, separation, or death, can be so stressful that it can be a cancer catalyst. A change in jobs, lifestyles or living quarters can be stressors as well.

Everyone handles stress differently, and symptoms vary from person to person. Some common reactions that might be stress-related are: upset stomach, constant fatigue, depression, headaches, a feeling of hopelessness, or abuse of food, alcohol, or drugs. Whatever the symptoms, stress can be hazardous to your health and should be taken seriously.

Stress management is a necessity. Consultants often get calls from companies or corporations that recognize that their employees are suffering from job burnout due to stress. Through various forms of education they can give their employees the important "tools" to handle almost any situation that may arise during the working day--and this, of course, can mean, their homelife as well.

Our goal should be to educate people, through humor to handle stress in a more positive manner. Laughter is perhaps the most powerful "tool" when we are confronted with a situation that might cause anxiety. Humans are the only creatures endowed with the gift of laughter--unless you count the hyena or "Flipper." It has been proven over and over again that the more laughter we have in our lives, the better off we are physiologically, psychologically, and spiritually. What a wonderful gift!

Physiologically, laughter helps to control pain. It is obviously not a viable analgesic for severe pain, but it can help some patients with mild or moderate pain. Norman Cousins used laughter to give him hours of pain-free sleep while he battled a connective tissue disorder. Cousins said, "Laughter is suspected of assisting in the release of endorphins--the body's natural painkillers and it definitely reduces stress that can in some cases amplify pain."

Laughter increases relaxation. As laughter subsides, so does tension, until it's significantly lower. Humor can even break the anger cycle. When an inconsiderate driver cuts in front of you, don't blow your horn or shout unkind words. As I suggested in an earlier chapter, instead of the negative reaction, why not try something humorous. When that driver cuts in front, YOU CONTROL THE SITUATION!! I suggest you keep a pair of Groucho Marx glasses in the car for just such occasions! As you pass the rude driver, simply slip on the glasses and wave calmly as you drive by! I promise you he will laugh, and so will you. This is a perfect example of how laughter can distract attention and reduce tension which should be your goal when dealing with stressful situations.

Other methods for handling stress are:

1. Take a humor break anywhere. Tell people at work that instead of a coffee break you are going on a humor break! Read the comics or a funny book. Tell someone a joke. Whatever you do, just sit down, relax and have fun!

2. This method really goes over well with bosses: CALL IN WELL ONE DAY!!!

3. Put up a sign celebrating BGIM (be glad it's Monday) instead of TGIF.

4. Put a humor bulletin board up at work with a cartoon missing its caption. Encourage employees to write their own captions.

5. Brighten up a room with posters and funny signs.

6. Spend some time with a child to learn what is really delightful and fun about life!

7. Try hard to laugh when you are sad. Psychologist William James said, "We don't laugh because we're happy--we're happy because we laugh."

8. Try some non-competitive play. Play tennis or racquetball without scoring.

9. Write an entry each day in a humor journal for later reading.

10. Tell a joke to everyone you meet in one day.

11. Energize your life by acting like a five-year-old. Blow soap bubbles or read a fairy-tale book. Color a picture with crayons for fun!

12. Help someone with a problem, and you will forget about yours--at least for a while!

13. Wear your best dress or suit on Monday.

Businesses recognize the importance of having happy employees--and happy employees are more often healthy employees. Laughter enhances respiration and circulation. In addition, stress-related hormones may be suppressed through laughter. Armed with this new-found knowledge, more and more employers are recognizing that humor may have an impact on the number of sick days an employee may use and could thus reduce health-care costs. For all businesses, that is the bottom line.

A professor who teaches "Humor and Communications" at the University of Central Florida says that companies are becoming more and more attuned to employees' sociological needs. Professor Ed Wycoff states, "Managers are realizing the importance of interpersonal relations within business organizations, and humor is a key element in that."

Business managers may wish to read *The Light Touch: How to Use Humor for Business Success* (Simon & Schuster, $9.95, by Malcolm Kushner). Jokes, anecdotes, and tips, all designed to help "manage conflict, motivate employees, improve productivity, influence corporate culture, and improve letters, memos and reports" are in this little jewel of a book. Managers are finding that these suggestions pay off. Wycoff says, "When a person uses humor in a corporate meeting, it seems to punch a hole in all the pomposity and the artificial status. It takes the rigidity of the corporation away and makes everybody feel they are part of the team."

Some stress reduction methods that are perfect for the workplace:

1. Take a deep breath and count to ten.
   When stressors rush toward you, try this: Close your eyes, take a deep breath, and feel your breath filling your lungs. Count slowly to ten, release your breath, open your eyes, and return to your work.

2. Take a break away from work.
   A few minutes away can do a lot to relieve stress.
   Find two or three good "getaways."

3. Ask for help.
   Everyone needs help once in a while.
   Agree with yourself to ask supervisors or co-workers for help
   when you need it, and return the favor by helping them when
   you can.

Remember that everyone experiences stress. It is how we
handle it that is so important. The ability to laugh at ourselves
enables us to have a more stress-free-life, and this almost
guarantees a more enjoyable life. Let the little kid in all of us,
regardless of age, shine through!
    Play and have fun!

6
Laughing at Work and Keeping Your Job

Business is fun, and you'll do more business if you can see the humor in the daily work situation.   Robert S. Wieder

Three things prevent us from having fun in the work place: Bernie, Bertha and the Boss.

Bernie and Bertha are employees who somehow manage to find the negative in every situation. They could win an all-expense paid trip to the Bahamas in the middle of the winter and complain that the chicken dinner was cold on the first class airplane flight. Always looking at the dark side of things and forecasting disaster with every project assigned to them, Bertha and Bernie are not really happy until they find at least a little bit of bad in the best of things. They never have to worry about tomorrow because they already know that everything will turn out wrong. Flowers remind them of funerals, and they are constantly pulling today's clouds over tomorrow's sunshine. We all should write to our state representatives and request that a law be made to prevent them from marrying and having children!

A person with a true passion for life and zeal and optimism will venture into a restaurant without any money and expect to pay for his dinner with the pearl that he will find in his oyster! A person with vision will go fishing and take along a camera and a frying pan. And as Zig Ziglar says: "Go after Moby Dick in a rowboat with a jar of tartar sauce!" A real optimist is someone who falls from the sixteenth floor of a building and on the way down says, "So far, so good!" or a man who marries his secretary and still thinks that he is going to dictate to her!

People who possess true passion are often leaders in their fields. General Eisenhower said, "Leadership is deciding what has to be done and getting people to want to do it!" Well said! He captured the passion of the workforce with one sentence.

The most memorable and possibly the most passionate person that I ever met was a man they simply called Super

Dave. His impact on me has lasted for years. Super Dave was a janitor at a mall in Virginia Beach, Virginia. He characteristically wore a baseball cap low, covering his eyes. His large and bushy moustache almost covered his entire mouth. He would often follow shoppers and mimic their walk until a crowd noticed and would begin to laugh. When the unsuspecting victims turned to see what the commotion was all about, Dave would do an about-face and march in the opposite direction. His high jinks included marching in precision military drills with his broom as a rifle and polishing the trash cans with rapid fire accuracy. You see, Super Dave was a regular guy who took ordinary and somewhat boring work and turned it into an interesting and fun adventure, both for himself and others.

Word of Super Dave's antics spread throughout the community, and soon people came by carloads to see his antics and to shop at the mall. Dave was a genuine "plerker" (one who adds play to work). You may have seen Dave on the television programs <u>Real People</u> and <u>That's Incredible</u>.

Another man who made his job more interesting than it really was is a school bus driver from the South. His claim to fame was that he often dressed up as Elvis and sang on the bus while driving the children to school. He was so popular that children assigned to that bus very seldom missed a day of school. The kids loved him and his daily performances! I saw this remarkable man on the national television program, <u>Hard Copy</u>.

How can you inject more enthusiasm and passion in your work? I decided a long time ago that the secret to success is to decide what you really like to do and then do it or at least try to do it! When you meet an enthusiastic man or woman at work, take a moment to observe them; see what sets them apart from their co-workers. I am sure their reply would be that they really enjoy their work!

The average working person spends approximately one-third of their existence in the work place, and 1,784 of those workdays will be Mondays! If we must work, and we do, then why not enjoy ourselves and do a better job while we are at it!

Following are a few fun ideas that should bring more laughter where you work. Post them on a bulletin board, and see what happens!

Blow soap bubbles at your desk.

Learn to juggle scarves in your office.

Put jokes, funny stories, and cartoons in inter-office mail.

Make up fun riddles, and place them on toothpicks. Stick them on cookies or candy, and place them where the employees will enjoy them.

How about having everyone bring in their baby pictures for a bulletin board?

Use a Polaroid camera to catch other employees doing something funny and paste it up on a board with a caption.

Lighten up a staff meeting by starting with a funny story or something embarrassing that happened to you. This will probably lead to others chiming in with some of their experiences.

Start a "Humor Diary" at work and pass it around for others to write in also. They can read it when they are in need of a chuckle.

Start a "Humor Wish List," and put down all the funny things that you would like to see happen at work.

Begin a reward system at your work for those employees who do outstanding work. Make it fun and enjoyable for everyone involved! An employee at Sentara Norfolk General Hospital came up with an inexpensive system of rewarding her co-workers at meetings. When an employee came up with a money-saving idea, she gave them a Pay Day candy bar. If they completed a difficult project when or before it was due, she gave them a

Crunch Bar. If they came up with ideas and successfully gathered donations for a needy agency, then she gave them a Rally Bar. If they exhibited a good sense of humor and boosted morale on the job, they were rewarded with a Snickers Bar.

Still another group of workers put their heads together and came up with a plan to discourage other workers from coming in late. Late employees reduce profits and affect overall morale. One worker decided to serenade the tardy suspect.

Another chose to play "Chariots of Fire" when they came in late. A clever employee invented a "Late Lottery." Those on time bet on the arrival time and formed a pool for the offender. When the latecomer arrived, he or she had to pay a dollar to the person who came closest to their arrival time. My personal favorite was eliminating one parking space. As you might imagine, everyone scrambled to get there on time then!

One creative and productive worker suggested making a list of five goal-related tasks they wished to accomplish each day. If they finished only four, then they placed the remaining one on the next day's list. As each task was completed, they crossed it out with a fluorescent marker that implies "Hey, I really did something today!" Of course, along with work comes play. On the work list, they placed five items, and on the play list they placed ten fun-oriented items that they wanted to do that day. Ten to five seems fair to me!!

Let's think about what we have read so far. At the beginning of this chapter you read the statement: "There are three things in the workplace that prevent us from having fun: Bernie, Bertha, and the Boss." After reading about how to bring more laughter and fun into the workplace, how about the Boss? Well, we were saving the best for last!

Do you have a boss who makes statements such as these?

Wipe that smile off your face!

Stop fooling around and get back to work!

We don't pay you to socialize here!

I suppose you think this is funny, don't you?

Get up off that floor; you don't know where it's been!

If I let you go home early this afternoon, then everyone who has a heart attack will want to go home early, too!

Folks, I'll tell you that there probably isn't much that can be done about a person who makes statements like these, and I certainly wouldn't waste time worrying about them. What I can suggest that you do, however, is exact a form of non-verbal, non-threatening revenge. Just how do you go about this? Easy. Imagine, if you will, your boss jumping up and down, completely nude, while throwing a tantrum. Boy, if that doesn't put things in perspective, nothing will.

You can do the same thing if the boss is giving you a dressing down: simply imagine him standing there naked. Suddenly, you don't feel so bad because this person is saying something that is belittling or unkind to you. And, most importantly, you haven't had to do anything verbally or physically to your boss, thus saving your job! In other words, you can have your hurt and eat it too!!

Liz Curis Higgs, a popular workplace humorist, says it best about management: "Humor in the workplace should be approached in a 'From the Top Down' manner; employees will take their cue from you! Remember: Managers who laugh, last. And customers who laugh, come back for more. Funny business really is good business!"

According to the Research Institute of America, corporate attitudes toward employees with a sense of humor were recently surveyed by Robert Half Associates. Personnel directors and vice presidents of 100 large corporations were asked if employees who had a sense of humor, did better, the same as, or worse than workers who have little or no sense of humor. Eighty-four percent felt that employees who openly displayed a sense of humor did much better.

This statement reinforces my comments about humor in the workplace. Not only do employees exhibit a better attitude about their job, but their job performance is also better than an employee who is surly, unhappy, and unable to laugh at stressful situations.

Dr. Beverly M. Henry says: "Fun and humor are integral parts of good health, leadership and professional action. The research...clearly supports this proposition. So does everyday observation. Where people are having fun together, where there is at least a modicum of laughter, humor, and playfulness, there is also a greater enthusiasm for the tasks at hand."

7
Funny Stuff for Teachers

Creative Use of Humor in Education

Adults average 15 laughs a day. Children laugh 400 times a day. Somewhere between childhood and adulthood, we lose 385 laughs a day.

Allen Klein

Our first grade class was heading for the cafeteria where we were to sample the day's surprise cuisine.

"*Mr. Kissell?*" said February (Yes, that is her real name. Guess what month she was born?), sounding distressed.

"*Yes?*" I replied, in a hurry to beat Mrs. Anderson's class to lunch.

"*Mr. Kissell, there are ants in my lunch box.*"

Ants in her lunch box? OK, probably just a few. I'll just brush them off, and we will be on our way, right?

Wrong. Opening her lunch box, I was greeted with an insect collector's dream. An entire colony had found a home in this precious girl's lunch. I quickly rinsed the ants down the drain, unable even to save her drink.

Tiny tears flowed down her cheeks as she gazed up at me for a solution to her problem. "*February,*" I said, "*the lunch box is all cleaned out. When we pass the office on the way to the cafeteria, you can slip in and ask for a charge slip.*" About midway in the sentence I began to aggressively scratch my back, legs, and stomach.

"*What's wrong?*" February asked.
The itching increased. "*I don't know,*" I said. "*I think I have ants in my pants!*"

As you might guess, I really didn't have ants in my pants, and February no longer had a disaster on her hands. I had used laughter to reduce her doubts and fears, not to make fun of her dilemma, but to alleviate her anxiety. The ants were disposed of; lunch was solved with a charge slip; and humor provided by the presence of ants in the teacher's pants.

Many times each day, teachers encounter similar problems in their classrooms. Often, a kind word and a bit of wit provides a simple solution. This can teach a child a valuable lesson not found in any textbook--the lesson of using humor to help out a stressful situation. We need to teach children that it's all right to laugh at our daily problems. In fact, it's healthy! Laughter is the great communicator and stress reliever.

If adults laugh only 15 times a day and children laugh 400 times, what's happened to the other 385? Perhaps they've been lost in such statements as *"You must take your job more seriously!"* And let's not forget the ever popular *"Firings will continue until morale is raised."*

Statements and attitudes like these really do affect our morale and, ultimately, our teaching ability. Let's face it: a happy teacher is a productive teacher! That's why it's so important to insert humor into as many lesson plans as possible.

I remember one student named Tory who was frightened by books. He could not make any sense out of these strange things that decorated our kindergarten classroom.

After lunch one day, I prepared for that favorite event-- story time. I reached behind me for the book that was customarily there and found, to my surprise, that it was gone. Not wanting to lose any time searching, I reached for and picked up an imaginary book. "Today's story is about the invisible book." The children sat in disbelief as I read the title and began to turn the imaginary pages while reading. Several of the students had the strangest looks on their faces, looks of surprise and confusion, looks that seemed to say, "Mr. K. has finally gone off his rocker."

After I completed the story, a boy spoke up. "No way, Mr. K! There was no book there!"

"Really?" I replied. "Tell me: what was the name of the book?"

"*The Invisible Book*," he said.
"What was the name of the author?" He even remembered it. I asked the others the names of the characters, the plot, the problem, and how it was solved. They knew all the answers. Why? Because they had to rely on their imagination to see the cover, pages, and the pictures.

When we completed the discussion, I set the imaginary book on the chalkboard ledge and told them that during center time they could take turns reading it to each other, but no fighting over the book. I couldn't believe that they actually started to fight, each wanting to read the imaginary book to each other.

Tory eventually had his chance, and to my delight, sat perched on a stool singing and sharing the book with the others. He made up an entire story with pictures while the others sat in amazement. They were entertained by his newly acquired skill as a master storyteller. Later, to my surprise, Tory's lack of anxiety about the imaginary book was transferred to real books. He found that he could recognize several works from time to time and talk on them. I believe that humor played a key role in his reading development.

Laughter does not have to be limited to the classroom. In our school, humor has spread into the administration office. Lou Page, our assistant principal, gives a typical example of counseling two students involved in a fight. The aggressor was discussing what had started the fight. A student said something offensive to this child, and in retaliation he began physically assaulting the other child.

"I want you to say, Mr. Page, you have a big nose," said Page. The child sat in confusion.

"Don't be afraid to say it; you won't get into any trouble," Page assured him.

The child reluctantly whispered it.

"I want you to yell it at me."

The student did. Page then said, "Am I mad? Am I hitting you?"

As the discussion progressed, the student realized that words can't really hurt and that there were other ways to respond than with violence.

Humor can also be shared with the faculty as well. In our lounge each month, I placed an enlarged cartoon mounted on cardboard with the caption removed. At the top of the poster I attached a marker and place a title: *Write Your Own Caption!* Teachers had the opportunity to express their creativity. Many times their captions were much better than the original. We have great fun with this activity.

Faculty members have discovered that there are many humorous activities that can lighten up the educational process. One teacher had a day set aside for "Show and Smell," a time to bring fun and smelly things in a zip-lock bag. The entire hallway radiated with pleasant smells. Throughout the day visitors were drawn to the classroom like bees to a flower.

Another teacher assigns the students to bring in funny or happy newspaper articles. Still another uses knock-knock jokes as a writing assignment. The students write, edit, re-write, and present them to the class orally.

Our faculty lounge is used during lunchtime for a "Did I tell you the one about...?" or "One of my students said the funniest thing." Do you have a lounge filled with complaints and negative comments? Change it into a fun place to be where you can get your batteries charged instead of drained. If necessary, you may want to have a table set aside and labeled NO GRIPING TABLE.

As educators, working in classrooms filled with children that suffer from every problem imaginable, we find ourselves needing our sense of humor renewed and fed each day. Using laughter in the classroom and with the faculty will brighten your day as well as that of those around you. The learning climate will be enhanced and the retention rate of the students increased. Laugh a little--and learn a lot.

Fun Things for the Classroom

· Place a joke or riddle on the board each day.

· Write jump-rope rhymes using rap or chants.

· Rewrite a fairy tale changing the main character, setting, etc.

· Rewrite a fairy tale or popular story using your students' names in the place of the characters' names.

· Announce a riddle each day on the public-address system. At the end of the day read the best answers sent in to the office.

· Have a "show and smell" day where students bring in great things to smell in a plastic baggy.

· Have the students bring in happy or funny articles from newspapers ready to read or let them tell the main idea to the class.

· Collect and write knock-knock jokes.

· Include jokes in written tests to relax students.

· Take candid-camera shots. Post and invite good-natured captions or make a book of them.
· Create a story about a monster; draw pictures of what it looks

like. Maybe even build it in art class.

· Have students write the "best practical joke" story.

· Write reports on comedians or others in the humor field.

· Write a humor dictionary with just funny words and their definitions.

· Condense a funny quote book.

· Use magic tricks to begin a lesson.

· Provide a "humor center" where students can sit and read funny stories or draw their own cartoons.

· Assign students to keep a diary of funny jokes and stories they have heard or read.

· Make animal balloons for children as rewards for good behavior.

Experienced and seasoned teachers remark that the realization that they're good teachers is often very subtle. This dawns slowly on a teacher when they find themselves praising an automobile mechanic: "Say, I like the way you did that!" Or perhaps they hum the ABCs when searching for a name in the telephone book. And you know immediately that you are in the presence of a great teacher when their immediate reaction to someone cutting in front of them in the bank line - "Hey, you cut me!" However, the greatest example of thorough training in the teaching profession is the ability to drink three cups of coffee at 8:00 a.m. and to hold it until 3:45 p.m.!

Let me share a few side notes.

Challenge No. 1 Be A Communicator!!!

(Notice that we are not using the word "rule." The word seems so harsh, and we want to think of them as opportunities and challenges!)

There are many times that we as adults forget how a child really thinks and feels. Brenda Parker says it all in her poem

Him Took Us Ball From We

"Are you we teacher?"
The little girl asked with excitement in her voice
"Yes, I'm your teacher," I replied. "I'm so happy that you're here."

Suddenly the little girl began to cry.
What could the matter be?
"That mean boy over there!" she screamed,
"Him took us ball from we!"

Well, this scenario I'd experienced before
though in a different setting.
I encouraged the little boy to share,
but no respect was I getting.

Angrily, the little boy shouted,

"Me not in your class, and you not us teacher!"

Somehow we weren't communicating,
Was it I or he?

Having patiently observed his behavior I wondered,
What could the matter be?
So, firmly and lovingly
Into his eyes
while on my knee
"Yes, me am us teacher," I said, "Now give us ball to
we!"

This poem really rings true!! We as communicators must learn
to communicate with children on their level.

Dr. Peter Alsop wrote a song entitled *"My Little Clock."* It is
sung by his young daughter. She tells the listener that she has a
little clock just as adults have big clocks, but big clocks somehow seem more important than little clocks. Little clocks are
often pushed aside. The wonderful words in this song stand as
a poignant reminder of the difference between children and
adults.

· · · · · ·

I liked the way a school secretary communicated to the faculty
about the constant complaints about the school copier. She
made a list of the most frequently asked questions and posted
this note on a broken copier:

The Copier Is Out of Order!

YES   We Have Called The Service People.

YES They Will Be In Sometime Soon.

NO   I Cannot Fix It.

**NO   I Do Not Know How Long
It Will Take.**

NO   I Do Not Know What Caused It.

NO   I Do Not Know Who Broke It.

YES   We Are Keeping It.

**NO   I Do Not Know What You Are Going
To Do Now.**

It seems like only yesterday that my little girl Andrea turned six. While shopping at a mall, I spotted a clock on the wall of a store. Wanting to test her ability at telling time, I asked her what time it was. The clock was very large and had Roman numerals on it. Andrea paused for a moment and sadly admitted that she could not read the numbers on the clock. I asked her why, and she replied that it had "sticks" on it! Of course, what a wonderful, honest answer from a child!

Another time, my daughter Melanie was given an extremely large balloon with a face drawn on it. Somehow the balloon ran into a snag, which resulted in a huge explosion. Melanie was very upset, and the tears began to flow. I felt that a simple balloon didn't warrant such emotion until she explained how she felt. She said, "Daddy, it was like my best friend just blew up!" To my daughter, the balloon was her best friend. Since I am both a teacher and father, these two happenings reminded me how important communicating with a child is.

Communication skills are important in dealing with people of all ages. I had a college professor named Dr. Rosalie Kiah who became one of my favorite teachers while I was cramming a four-year degree into seven years!! Dr. Kiah knew how to communicate. In each of her classes we were treated to 10 minutes of "chin wagging." She would tell us of her exotic trips abroad or the current status of her favorite basketball team. She was loved by everyone for her spontaneity and genuine concern for us as people, not just as students. She often placed humorous questions in the feared mid-term and final tests, which were a delightful surprise and also helped relieve some of our stress.

I recently read an account of an English teacher whose class played a practical joke on her. While her back was turned, the students dropped their books to the floor in unison. Realizing what had happened, the teacher raced to her desk, picked up a book, dropped it to the floor, and said, "Sorry I was late!" What a clever comeback!!

Challenge No. 2 Teach Life

Teacher handbooks printed for school personnel often state that one of the characteristics of a good teacher is a "good sense of humor." However, there are no specific ways that teach the art of humor.

Remember this poem?

> No written word or mortal plea
> Can teach young hearts what they should be
> Nor all the books upon the shelves
> But what the teachers are themselves!

The poem could have been written at any time; it will always be relevant! Why can't we teach children about life? And why don't we teach children with dedication, desire, and most important, originality.

Two janitors worked in a public school in New York City. They became friends with many of the students, each taking time to share their opinions and concerns with the kids. When it came time for the seniors to graduate, they requested that their janitors speak at the commencement exercises. What an honor to these two people! Both made a difference in the lives of the students, a real accomplishment with teens today! They took time to listen and talk, something that so many teachers don't do today. You have seen those two janitors on the Oprah Winfrey show!

Are we going to teach objectives that are not found in the curriculum, things that we wished our teachers had taught us? I hope so! Have you ever met someone in the field who has the attitude that they are "just a teacher"? Remember the mental patient in the movie Teacher? He somehow wandered into a high school and was put to work as a substitute teacher. One of the first things the "teacher" did was to throw all the books out the window! The students loved it!! Next he dressed as Abraham Lincoln and delivered the Gettysburg Address by memory. Later he dressed as General Washington; he formed the desks into a boat and sailed with the students across the Potomac. Don't you think the students retained more information from this type of interactive, inductive learning?

Challenge No. 3 Energize!!

Who is the person you must take care of?

Who is the person you need to entertain?

Who is the person you need to make laugh the most?

You guessed it right if you thought of yourself right away! We have to give ourselves an added boost in the morning before greeting the students. If we are "energized" by laughter and good feelings, the final result will be a higher level of productivity and enthusiasm, which should ultimately lead to a better relationship with your students.

Believe it or not, a simple thing like wearing your best and brightest clothing to school on Monday can make a positive impact that will last throughout the day!

Smiling before you address each student will add "miles of smiles" to both you and your students!

Complimenting another teacher or student will give them that extra spark which may be needed to survive the day!

Increasing your "comic vision" is simply watching for humorous situations on the way to work. These can be shared over and over again for instant chuckles.

My favorite is a giant billboard near our school that read:
Are you Illiterate? Call 1-800-CAN-READ! (Whom could this sign be for?)

A sign on a post-office door window read:
NO PETS ALLOWED !
Then on the lower panel of the door another sign read:
EXCEPT SEEING EYE DOGS
(Now I ask you: whom might this sign be for--unless the dog called the 1-800 number?)

While I was visiting my parents during a school holiday, a friend passed away, and I was asked to be a pall bearer. Signing the guest register, I discovered free post cards from the funeral home. I took six of the cards and wrote my best friends little notes saying **HAVING FUN, WISH YOU WERE HERE!!** Whenever anyone talks about a funeral, I can't help but chuckle over that memory.

My Favorite Teaching Stories

In my science class in college our professor was instructing us on how to teach science to high school students. The discussion centered on the Latin term "iso." The professor asked us for examples of "iso" as a prefix. Some of the answers were isometric, isotherm and isobaric. I raised my hand and gave the answer "isocream." A stillness descended into the room, and I will always remember the surprised teacher glaring at me as he said, "Kissell, it is my hope that in your first year of teaching you have a student just like you!" He was a wonderful teacher who turned out to have psychic powers--the first year of teaching, I actually had five students just like me!

My first year as a teacher was a great challenge; after only one month, my students suddenly disappeared! The housing development behind my school was torn down, and the people were relocated to other areas of the city. Because of these changes, I was put on an "auction block" and given to the highest bidder. Another principal who needed a kindergarten teacher "won" me, and I was promptly moved to another school. What made this move so challenging was that there were five kindergarten teachers with 30 children in each class. To say that these teachers were happy to see me is an understatement! The principal gave the teachers permission to remove five of "their very best" students for the new teacher--me. As you might imagine, these "very best" students turned out to be challenges, and I learned very early in my teaching career to use humor to educate and amuse them. I also used humor to help myself through some stressful, difficult situations. For the "big day," I was waiting at the door to my classroom clad in a tuxedo. My reasoning was that if it was going to be a formal evaluation, at least let me dress for it. The principal, however, didn't seem to be amused by either my attire or my sense of humor!

The end of the year was finally near, and I was beginning to feel more self-confident. In a discussion of family units one day, the conversation turned to twins. I told the students that I had a twin brother who was also a teacher, and if they wished, I would ask him to be their teacher the following Monday. The kids were so excited! I was also really excited, but for a different reason: I don't have a twin brother! When Monday arrived, I dressed in a suit and tie, slicked back my hair with a new part on the side, and wore my old glasses. When the students first saw me, they were very shy. Some were nonbelievers; however, I quickly convinced them that I was my twin brother by calling them incorrect names and having to use name tags. When it came time to collect homework that had been assigned to them on Friday, they informed me that my "brother" had said nothing about it! When Tuesday arrived and I asked the children for their homework, they replied, "Your brother said we didn't have any homework, and we like him better!" This episode remains one of my fondest memories of teaching and is also my favorite practical joke of all time! If you have a memorable experience to share with me, please let me know. I can always use more great material for the next workbook.

A group of teachers in Richmond, Virginia, came up with this proclamation:

The Sanity in Education Act\Amendments

In an attempt to promote the undeniable but sorely abused rights of the teachers of middle schools and to draw nationwide attention to the "closet" issue of Adolescent Harassment of Middle School Educators, we, the aforementioned teachers, do hereby and forthwith proclaim:

[Item 1] No students shall be permitted herein to return from an absence of 23 consecutive school days and then innocently inquire, "Did we do anything?"

[Item 2] Grim laughter shall, herein, be a fitting and acceptable response to students requesting three weeks of work in advance because they are leaving the next day for educational excursions to Honolulu, Aspen, or Disney World.

[Item 3] A posse of veteran teachers wielding rapid-fire detention notices shall be dispatched to round up students lost, meandering, or journeying on The Paper Trail.

Amendments

[Item 4] No students shall be permitted to come to class mindless, bookless, paperless, and writing-implementless and say, "Do we need anything?"

[Item 5] No student shall be permitted to say, "I missed the first 3 minutes of class on the first Monday of September, so I shouldn't have to take the test on Thursday, March 16th."

[Item 6] An annual lottery shall be held in order to choose a student from The Ten Most Wanted List of Worst Behaved Students (as compiled by teachers). The "winning" student shall be honored at an assembly wherein designated teachers shall hurl dusty erasers at the honoree.

[Item 7] Runners-up on The Ten Most Wanted List of Worst Behaved Students shall be sent, at the close of the school year, up a "Slow Creek Without A Paddle."

[Item 8] The Student Handbook shall be amended to ban jammed lockers.

[Item 9] It will hereby be a felony to trip teachers by placing book bags around their necks albatross-like. (See "Rime of the Ancient Mariner") Note: This is, by the way, an outstanding team name.)

[Item 10] To eliminate the dreaded "Do we need our book today?", turnstiles with scanners shall be placed in classroom doorways to allow only those with proper supplies to enter. All others have to just go away.

[Item 11] An affirmative answer to the "Is this an emergency?" question, shall hereby be countered with a referral to the school urologist, instantly inserting the student on Step #1 of the T.P. Trail.

[Item 12] Debate by honors students over the validity, wording, and fairness of True-False Test questions shall be limited to 24 minutes per question. Teacher rebuttal may last up to 30 minutes or 10 eye-rolling gestures by students or whichever comes first.

[Item 13] Blatant disdainful glances shall hereby be fitting and proper responses to students heard uttering the following: (a) "Will this be on the test?" (b) "Why do we have to learn this?" (c) "You never told us about it." and (d) "Is that a run in your stocking or some kind of rash?"

[Item 14] Photocopied transcripts of "Jeopardy" shall herein be a definitive and appropriate answer to students asking, "When will we ever use this in REAL life?" Also, disgust.

[Item 15] The collection of field trip monies shall be increased from 56 to 75 days following the announcement of said trip; additionally, delinquent field trip fees may now accrue simple interest not to exceed 7 percent.

Hold still; this won't hurt a bit!
Now which tooth was hurting?
You failed to make the 50th percentile!
Don't worry, we have just the thing for teaching anxiety!
I've heard of B-TAP, but this is ridiculous.
We have just the cure for teaching anxiety.

Teachers at Suburban Park Elementary School in Norfolk, Virginia, had the opportunity to write their own caption for the cartoon above. This is a great activity for the teachers' lounge. Simply remove the printed caption and write the invitation for the teachers to "write your own caption!" This really inspires creativity!

Creative Cartoons

Let your students guess what the following cartoons are.
Perhaps they could work in teams. How do they feel when they
are finished? Do they feel an accomplishment for the cartoons
that they guessed?

1. CUTTING (crossed out)	2. GAS AGE	3.
4. E inside square	5. Kick	6.
7. N.Y. 3:45 A.M. / N.Y. 7:30 P.M.	8. B U L L	9.
10. S H S H SHSHS	11.	12.
13. LOOKING THE FUTURE THE FUTURE	14.	15. Joes

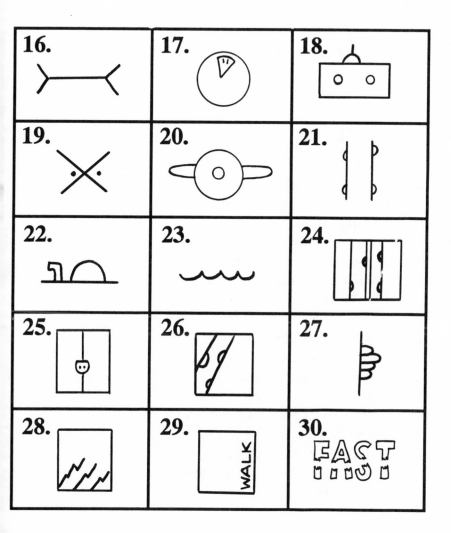

Creative Cartoons Answers

1.   Cutting edge
2.   Gas shortage
3.   Polar bear in snowstorm
4.   "East" side
5.   Drop kick
6.   Hopscotch
7.   New York Times
8.   Sitting bull
9.   Snorkeler
10. Shell
11. Cutting corners
12. Spider on mirror
13. Looking to the future
14. Ants marching up a hill
15. Sloppy Joes
16. Two birds fighting over a worm
17. Bug looking out of a can
18. Baby eating licorice in a drawer
19. Two fish kissing
20. Spanish American riding a bicycle
21. Bear climbing a tree
22. Fat man smoking in bed
23. Snorkeler underwater
24. Two giraffes kissing
25. Pig with its nose caught in an elevator
26. Giraffe walking by a window
27. Inside view of Napoleon's jacket
28. Soldiers walking by a window
29. Sidewalk
30. Breakfast

The following are a few "Funny Assignments"
to be used in the School of Life.
These assignments are designed to
increase your L.P.M. (Laughs Per Minute),
brighten your day, and bring more
humor into your life.

Start a **"Humor Journal."** Each day try to write something
funny inside it, such as a joke, a story, or your most embarrassing moment that day. Use it to reflect upon when you're in a
blue mood.

. . . .

Giving a power presentation at work with visual aids? Use a
toilet plunger for a pointer, listeners are sure to remember
your part of the talk.

Include a funny story or cartoon in inter-office mail. Those who read it will be sure to remember the message.

. . . . . .

Drive to work in reverse. See all the exciting scenery that you have been missing?

Call in well one day. Just tell your boss that you're feeling so great that you're not coming into work!

Keeping a set of juggling bags or scarves in your desk drawer. When times get tough, the tough get juggling.

Wear Groucho Marx glasses while driving to work. What a stitch. Look at all those crazy stares!

. . . .

While your banker is counting out a large stack of bills, start counting with them--then begin to count in reverse. Why do they get so angry?

. . . .

Buying an airline ticket? Ask them if they give "Frequent Survivor Points" for this flight.

. . . .

Photograph employees in a candid camera style, and post a collage of these photos.

Wait until your spouse is asleep, then turn on two flashlights, shine them in his or her face and yell,"Truck!!!"
Caution! Make sure you know CPR before trying this one.

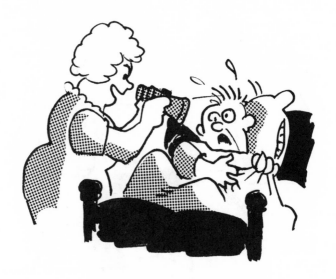

Fun Things
from Newspapers

Dear Abby,

I have been dating the same man for over a year and we are now engaged. I found out last week that he has a wooden leg. Should I break it off?

A freighter off the coast of North Carolina has been reported sunk. It was carrying a cargo of yo-yos. It went down 27 times.

The first police precinct was broken into recently. The burglar was reported taking all the toilet seats. And the police have nothing to go on.

A customer in an exclusive hotel was locked out of his room without any clothes on. He ran to the front desk, grabbed a piece of paper, and hid in a phone booth while calling 911. When the police arrived, they found the embarrassed man covering himself with just an application for an American Express card. When the company was interviewed for a comment, their reply was that they cover all essentials.

To the thief who stole my nine-dollar hitch coupler: I hope your boat breaks in half in midstream and your mother is unsuccessful in attracting help as she runs barking along the shore.

LOST AND FOUND: Lost dog, blind in one eye, has only 3 legs, broken tail and neutered. Answers to the name of "Lucky."

Practical Jokes
I Have Known

Take time to notice the silly things around the world today, and take heart that the oldest form of entertainment is alive and well today in every small city and metropolis. You may not be a comic, but you sure can have lots of laughs with the practical joke!

Have you ever found yourself waiting at a stop light and a police officer pulls up next to your car? Have some fun and hide your face by using your jacket or a book; you'll make a new friend soon.

If you're pulled over at night by a police person, shine a flashlight in their face, and ask if you can help them; guaranteed delight. (By the way, did you know in major cities they are placing police personnel in pizza trucks so that when you call 911 they can get there within 30 minutes, or it's $3 off your next ticket?)

Traveling on the interstate? Have you ever seen a sign that says STOP! CLEAN REST ROOMS AHEAD! Do it, and have loads of laughs. Passing through a pay toll? Pay the attendant an extra coin for the person behind you, and watch in the rear-view mirror as the new found friend breaks the sound barrier trying to catch up with you to see who paid his toll. When he does pull up to your side, look at him with the Groucho glasses on...touche.

Dining out? Why not introduce yourself to the waiter and say, "Hello, my name is _____ and I'll be your customer for the evening." Ordering pizza? Ask how many pieces the large pizza is cut into--12? Can you cut it in 8 pieces? I can't eat 12.

At home when the phone rings and it's a telephone solicitor? Say "Thank goodness, I thought you were another bill collector." Sure enough, they will remove your name from their list.

Answer your phone, and act like an answering machine complete with the beep. Halfway through the message, ask them to repeat their message and see how long it takes for them to catch on.

Do you like to fly? I'm on the "frequent survivor" plan myself. Ever see the shy guy in the airport holding up a sign with a passenger's name on it? Greet the sign holder as if you were the person they were waiting for. Chat a bit; discuss the flight; and then bid them a good day. Can you imagine their surprise when they discover that you are not the person they are waiting for? What a panic!

Finding yourself writing a check for $10, inquire as to the charge for a returned check. If it's $15, say, "So, I should make it out for $25?"

How about a visit to the dentist? When the mirror is in your mouth, blow on it, causing it to steam up. What a scream!

Going to a shotgun wedding? Be original and throw puffed rice.

How about visiting an antique store and saying, "Hey, what's new?"

Find an empty Nativity scene after Christmas, and place a sign on it saying, MOVED TO EGYPT.

Find yourself at a great mystery movie? When you leave the building, face the crowd in line for the next show and yell, "They all died in the end."

Flying somewhere and find yourself wanting to be alone, but a talkative person is sitting next to you? When they ask you what type of work you do, simply reply to them that you sell insurance. Trust me, you won't hear a peep out of them for the rest of the flight.

Want the seat next to you on the plane to stay empty? Sit down next to it, and place the airsick bag on your lap. Mess up your hair a bit and wrinkle your clothing. When they see you, they will surely ask to be moved by the attendant!

Have fun, my friends. Venture forth and meet someone new and exciting, and write to tell a relative, friend or me about it! Please have a wonderful life, and remember to look for the humor in all things. It is God's gift to us.

Things in Life
I Don't Understand
and Wonder About

Watches with the year on them

"Jumbo Shrimp"

Why our parents asked us if we "wanted" a "spanking"

Shop teachers with missing fingers

Librarians with hearing aids

Military intelligence

Where are all the Susan B. Anthony dollars?

Why is the word "abbreviation" so long?

Why do we abbreviate the word "July"?

Why do women apply makeup while driving?

Why do men read books while driving?

What does "pretty ugly"really mean?

What does "awfully good" mean?

Do people really "rest" in rooms?

If most traffic accidents occur within five miles of home, why don't more people move?

When they ship styrofoam, what do they pack it in?

If every fifth child born in the world is Chinese, and you already have four children. What will happen next?

What is "occasional irregularity?"

If a person lives at the end of a one-way street, how do they move?

They say that bread always falls butter-side down. They say that a falling cat (which is a dog with a bad attitude) always lands on its feet. What would happen if you buttered your bread, taped it on the back of the cat, then dropped the cat out a window?

Is "Lamaze" French for scream?

Is "cul-de-sac" French for dead end?

Do executioners use an alcohol swab before giving a lethal injection?

Why do people always pick the bathroom stall next to yours in the airport when there are 15 empty ones?

What Kids Say to God

Dear God,

In Sunday School they told us what to do. Who does it when you are on vacation?

Instead of letting people die and make new ones, why don't you just keep the ones you got now?

Do animals use you or is there someone else for them?

I wish you would not make it so easy for people to come apart, i had 3 stitches and a knot.

I'm doing the best I can!

Did you mean for giraffes to look like that or was it an accident?

I didn't think orange went with purple until I saw the sunset you make on Tuesday. . . that was cool!

About the Author

From a very early age, Steve Kissell found the need to entertain and amuse people. Even as a "little person" he felt best when people were laughing and enjoying themselves - even at his expense! After joining the Navy, Kissell harnessed his enormous drive, enthusiasm, and love of comedy into a variety of children's characters and soon built up a loyal following who enjoyed his performances and shows.

Never one to sit still for long, Kissell embarked on a teaching career after leaving the Navy, where he proceeded to mold unsuspecting kindergarten and first graders into his own image- a scary thought!

Steve says that the path to becoming a humorist and speaker seemed a natural progression after years of perfecting his craft as a clown and magician. Early in his lecturing career, Kissell read about and observed the deepening concern doctors and health officials had about the possible link between stress and illness. Conducting his own unofficial surveys and research, Kissell found data to support his beliefs that stress can cause illnesses, both emotional and physical. He also found that companies and corporations were coming around to the fact that a stressed-out employee can be counterproductive while an employee who is relatively stress-free has fewer illnesses and a better work record.

Armed with this relatively new information, Kissell decided the time was right to take his message to a brand new audience. He has spoken in 23 states of which only two have asked him to leave!

Quality Presentations
Since 1956

Humor Resources

AMERICAN ASSOCIATION OF THERAPEUTIC HUMOR.
Publishes a quarterly newsletter and offers networking
opportunities. 9040 Forest View Road, Skokie, IL 60203-1913

CLOWNS OF AMERICA INTERNATIONAL.
National clown organization with a 6-times-per-year magazine,
The New Calliope. Clowns of America International, Inc.
PO Box 570, Lake Jackson, TX 77566-0570

CLOWN SUPPLIES. Catalogue sales of a wide variety of
costumes, props, and gags. M.E. Persson, 17 Chesley Drive,
Barringon, NH 03825

CURRENT COMEDY. Original humor you can use.
Newsletter twice monthly. Subscription office:
700 Orange Street, Wilmington, DE 19801

INSTITUTE FOR ADVANCEMENT OF HUMAN BEHAVIOR.
Annual three-day Laughter and Play conference.
4370 Alpine Road, Suite 108, Portola Valley, CA 94025

JEST FOR THE HEALTH OF IT. Workshops for health care
professionals, author, presentor, and clown. Patty Wooten,
P O Box 4040, Davis, CA 95617. (916) 758-3826.

LAUGHMAKERS MAGAZINE. A collection of articles and advertising for performing artists such as clowns, magicians, mimes, puppeteers, and storytellers.
 PO Box 160, Syracuse, NY 13215

PUBLISHERS CENTRAL BUREAU. Mail order catalogue distribution of videotapes of comedy classics. PO Box 1072, Department 205, Newark, NJ 07101-1072

STEVE KISSELL. Motivational humorist and national speaker. Provides keynotes, seminars and workshops on the use of humor in the workplace and personal life. 1227 Manchester Avenue, Norfolk, VA 23508-1122 Fax (804) 489-1587
Phone (804) 423-3867

THE HUMOR PROJECT. Research on humor, quarterly journal. Humor Project/Sagamore Institute, 110 Spring Street, Saratoga Springs, NY 12866

WHIM, WORLD HUMOR AND IRONY MEMBERSHIP. Annual interdisciplinary humor conference. Don Nilsen, Ph.D., English Department, Arizona State University, Tempe, AZ 85287

WHOLE MIRTH CATALOGUE. Provides access to humorous items, books, etc. 1034 Page Street, San Francisco, CA 94117

Humor Bibliography

Barry, Dave. *Babies and Other Hazards of Sex*. Pennsylvania: Rodale Press, 1984.

Bassindale, Bob. *How Speakers Make People Laugh*. West Nyack, NY: Parker, 1976.

Basso, B. with Klosek, J. *Lighten Up, Corporate America!* Los Angeles: New Breed Publications, 1986.

Black, Donald W. "Laughter." *Journal American Medical Association*, Vol. 252, No. 21 (December 7, 1984), pp. 2995-8.

Blumenfeld, Esther and Lynne Alpern. *The Smile Connection*. Englewood Cliffs, NJ: Prentice Hall, Inc., 1986.

Brilliant, Ashleigh. *I May Not Be Perfect, But Certain Parts of Me Are Excellent*. Santa Barbara: Woodbridge Press, 1979.

Brilliant, Ashleigh. *I've Given Up My Search for the Truth—I'm Now Looking for a Good Fantasy*. Santa Barbara: Woodbridge Press, 1979.

Brilliant, Ashleigh. *Love Me Now — Avoid the Rush*. Santa Barbara: Woodbridge Press, 1979.

Chapman, A.J. and Foot, H.C. (Eds.). *Humor and Laughter: Theory, Research and Applications*. London: Willey, 1976.

Cousins, Norman. *Anatomy of an Illness*. New York: W.W. Norton & Co., 1979.

Cousins, Norman. "Anatomy of an Illness." *New England Journal of Medicine,* Vol. 295 (1976), pp. 1458-1463.

Eberhart, E.T. *In the Presence of Humor: A Guide to the Humorous Life*. Salem, OR: Pilgrim House, 1983.

Fay, Allen, M.D.*Making Things Better by Making Them Worse*. New York: Hawthorn Books, Inc., 1978.

Fry, W.F.*Sweet Madness: A Study of Humor*. Palo Alto, CA: Pacific Books, 1963.

Fry, W.F. "Laughter and Health." *Encyclopedia Britannica, Medical and Health Annuals: Special Report*. USA: Encyclopedia Britannica, Inc., 1984, pp. 259-262.

Fry, W.F. and Salameh, Waleed A. (Eds.). *Handbook of Humor and Psycho-therapy*. Sarasota, FL: Professional Resource Exchange, 1986.

Fry, W.F.*Make 'Em Laugh: Life Studies of Comedy Writers*. Palo Alto, CA: Science and Behavior Books, 1975.

Gardner, J. "Laughing Matter? A Symposium of Studies on Humor as Communication." *Journal of Communication,* Vol. 26, No. 3 (Summer, 1976), p.102.

Gretjohn, Martin. *Beyond Laughter*. New York:
McGraw-Hill, 1957.

Gruner, C.R. *Understanding Laughter: The Workings of Wit and
Humor*. Chicago: Nelson-Hall, 1978.

Hageseth, Christian. *A Laughing Place*. Fort Collins, CO:
Berwick Publishing Co., 1988.

Hasset, James and Houlihan, John. "Different Jokes for Different
Folks." *Psychology Today,* Vol. 12 (January, 1979), pp. 64-71.

Hoban, Russell. *Bedtime for Frances*. New York:
Harper and Row, 1960.

*Humor: The Tonic You Can Afford. A Handbook on Ways of
Using Humor in Long-Term Care*. Monograph:
Andrus Volunteers Gerontology Center,
University of Southern California, Los Angeles, 1983.

Iapoce, M. *A Funny Thing Happened on the Way to the Board-
room: Using Humor in Business Speaking*. New York:
John Wiley & Sons, Inc., 1988.

International Journal of Humor Research. Walter de Gruyter,
Inc. 200 Saw Mill River Rd., Hawthorn, NY 10532.

Jacobson, Edith. "On the Child's Laughter and the Function of
the Comic." In *Depression,* pp. 42-65. New York:

International Universities Press, 1971.

Kissell, Steve. *Humorizing Employees Workbook*, 1992.

Klein, A. *The Healing Power of Humor*. Los Angeles: J.P. Tarcher, 1989.

Kohlberg, Lawrence (Hoffman, M. and Hoffman, L.W., Eds.). "Development of Moral Character and Moral Ideology." In *Review of Child Development Research Vol. 1*, pp. 383-431. New York: Sage, 1964.

Kris, Ernst. "Ego Development and the Comic and Laughter as an Expressive Process." In *Psychoanalytic Explorations in Art*, pp. 204-16; 217-39. New York: International Universities Press, 1952.

Kuhlman, T. *Humor and Psychotherapy*. Homewood, IL: Dow Jones, Irwin, 1984.

Laugh It Up. The American Association for Therapeutic Humor, 1441 Shermer Rd., Ste. 110, Northbrook, IL 60062.

Laughing Matters. The Humor Project, 110 Spring St., Saratoga Springs, NY 12866.

Lefcourt, H.M. *Humor and Life Stress: Antidote to Adversity*. New York: Springer-Verlag, 1986.

Loevinger, Jane. *Ego Development*. San Francisco, CA: Jossey-Bass, 1976.

Mindess, H. *Laughter and Liberation.* Los Angeles: Nash, 1971.

Moody, R.A., Jr.*Laugh After Laugh.* Jacksonville, FL: Headwaters Press, 1978.

Nahemow, L., et al., (Eds.).*Humor and Aging.* Orlando, FL: Academic Press, Inc., 1986.

Paulson, T. *Making Humor Work: Take Your Job Seriously and Yourself Lightly.* Los Altos, CA: Crisp Publications, 1989.

Peter, L. and Dana, B. *The Laughter Prescription.* New York: Ballentine, 1982.

Piaget, Jean. *The Child and Reality.* New York: Grossman, 1973.

Piaget, Jean (Tanner, J.M. and Inhelder, B., Eds.). "The General Problem of the Psychological Development of the Child." In *Discussion of Child Development, Vol. 4,* pp. 3-27. New York: International Universities Press, 1960.

Piaget, Jean. *The Psychology of Intelligence.* Paterson, NJ: Littlefield, Adams, 1963.

Ransohoff, Rita. "Some Observations on Humor and Laughter in Young Adolescent Girls." *Journal of Youth and Adolescence,*

Vol. 4 (June, 1975), pp. 155-70.
Redmore, Carlyn D. and Loevinger, Jane. "Ego Development in Adolescence: Longitudinal Studies." *Journal of Youth and Adolescence,* Vol. 8 (March, 1979), pp. 1-20.

Robinson, V. *Humor and the Health Professions.* Thorofare: Charles B. Slack, 1977.

Selman, Robert. "The Development of Conceptions of Interpersonal Relations: A Structural Analysis and Procedures for the Assessment of Levels of Interpersonal Reasoning Based on Levels of Social Perspective Taking." Unpublished manuscript. Cambridge, MA: Harvard-Judge Baker Social Reasoning Project, 1974.

Weinstein, M. and Goodman, J. *Playfair: Everybody's Guide to Competitive Play.* San Luis Obispo. CA: Impact Publishers, 1980.

Wolfenstein, Martha. *Children's Humor.* Glencoe, IL: The Free Press, 1954.

Ziv, A. *Personality and Sense of Humor.* New York: Springer, 1984.

Fun Things
I'd Like to Try